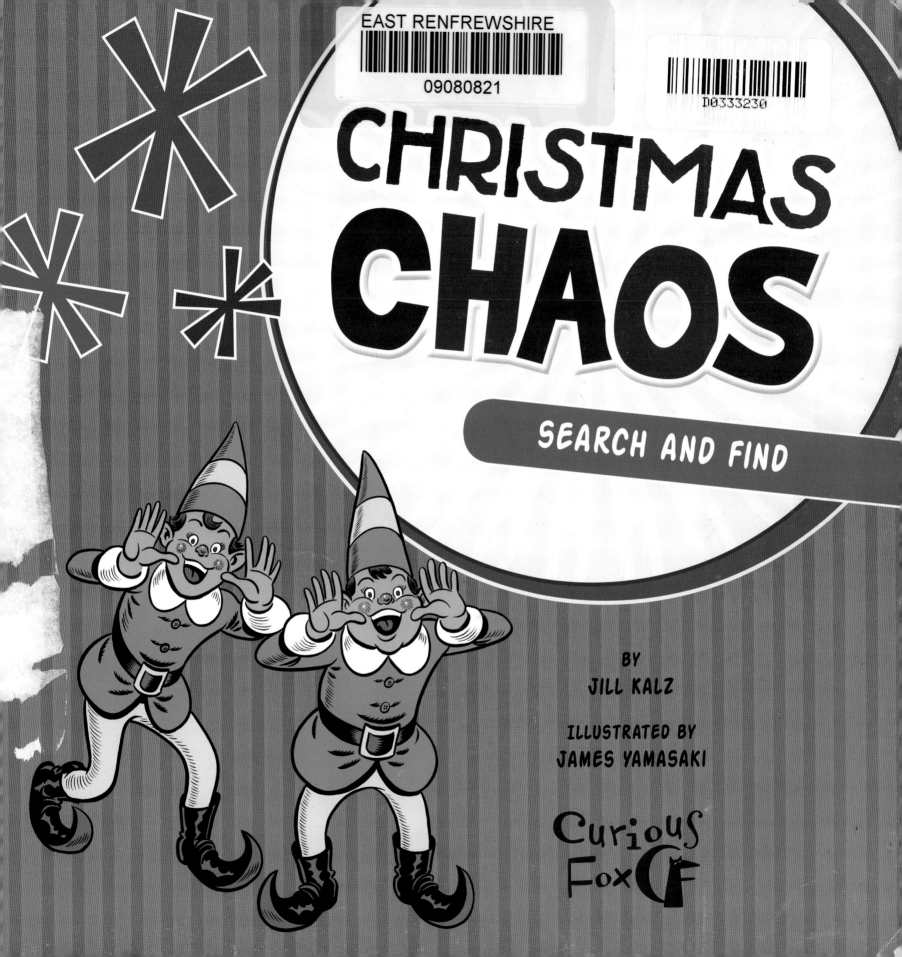

CHRISTMAS CHAOS

SEARCH AND FIND

BY
JILL KALZ

ILLUSTRATED BY
JAMES YAMASAKI

Curious Fox

First published in the UK by Curious Fox, an imprint of Capstone Global Library Limited,
7 Pilgrim Street, London, EC4V 6LB – Registered company number: 6695582

www.curious-fox.com

Designer: Lori Bye
Art Director: Nathan Gassman
Production Specialist: Danielle Ceminsky
The illustrations in this book were created digitally.

ISBN 978-1-78202-136-0
18 17 16 15 14
10 9 8 7 6 5 4 3 2 1

British Library Cataloguing in Publication Data
A full catalogue record for this book is available from the British Library.

Printed in China

WELCOME, SEARCHERS!

Look at the pictures and find the items on the lists. The first few puzzles are tricky. The next ones are even trickier. And the final puzzles are for the bravest seekers only. Good luck!

TABLE OF CONTENTS

Pause for Mr. Claus

- penguin
- Mrs. Claus
- doll's house
- rucksack
- angel
- tricycle

Go-Go Snow

- deer
- rabbit
- Santa
- toboggan
- snowman
- snowshoes

SKI PATROL

7

Cookie Crunch

- marble
- heart
- jingle bell
- wreath
- snowflake
- mitten

9

I See Ice

- chainsaw
- ice cream
- ladder
- bench
- lost mitten
- bucket of water

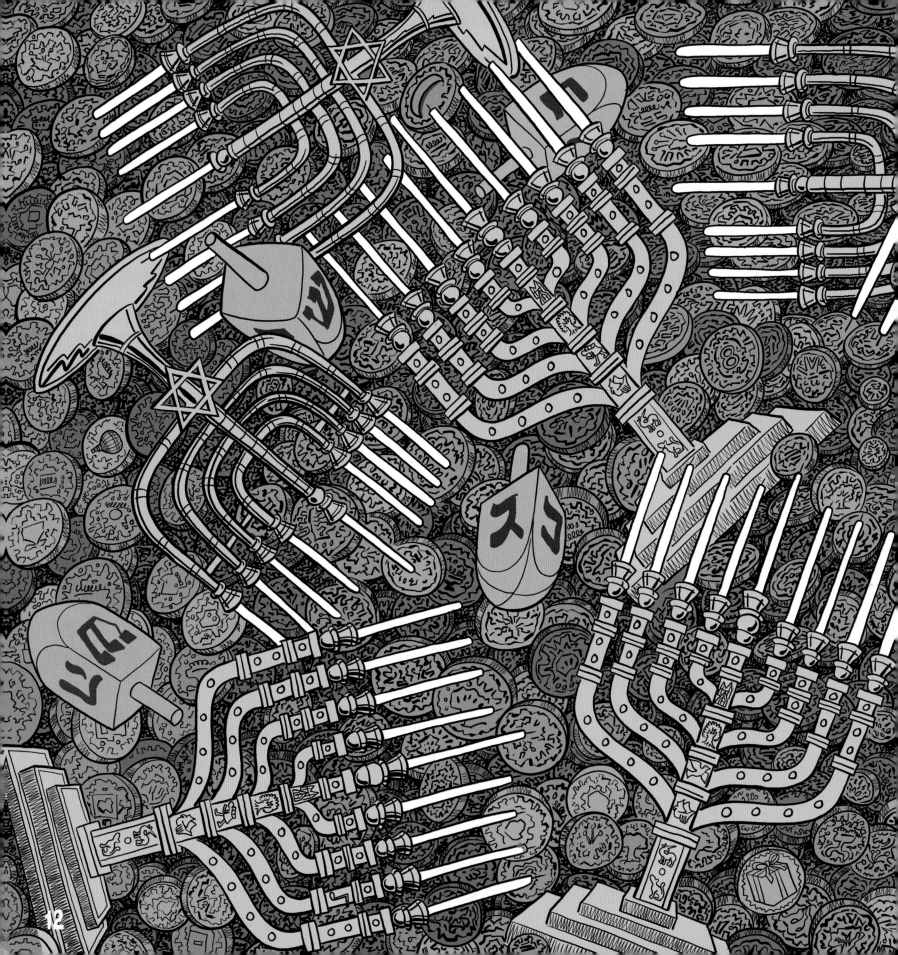

Hello, Hanukkah!

- gift
- moon
- dove
- number
- cookie
- musical note

13

Icy Delights

- snow shovel
- snowflake
- thermometer
- fish
- dog
- skis
- penguin
- fox
- snow angel

A Merry Morning

-  snowman
- nutcracker
- pig
- aeroplane
- mouse
- dog bone
- rugby ball
- strawberry
- elf

17

Night lights

words

red-nosed reindeer

gingerbread man

apple

candle

rocking horse

stocking

candy cane

pineapple

19

Colourful Kwanzaa

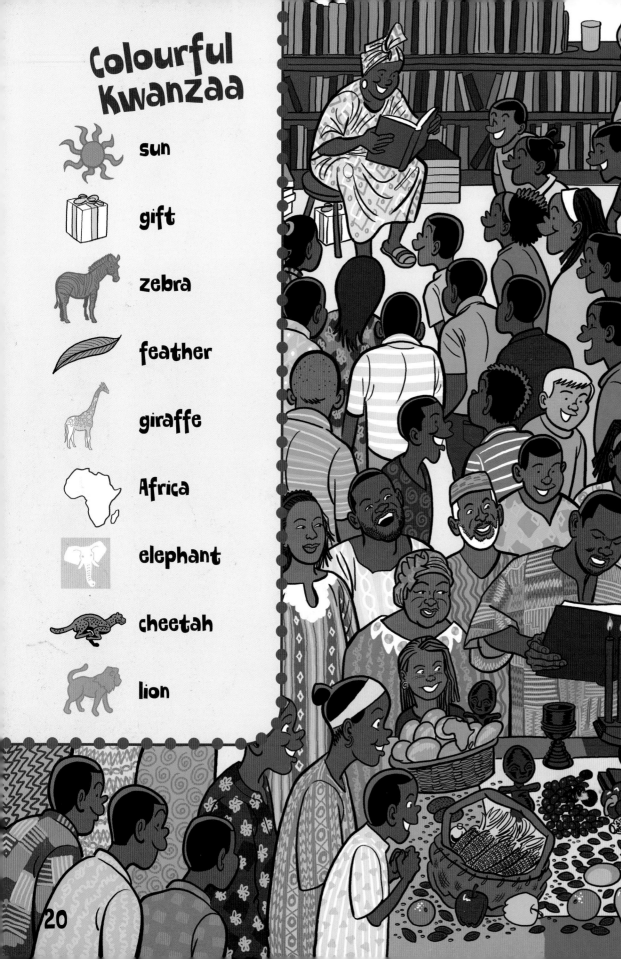

- sun
- gift
- zebra
- feather
- giraffe
- Africa
- elephant
- cheetah
- lion

20

Cool Yule

- pineapple
- mistletoe
- visor
- snowglobe
- dolphin
- holly
- owl
- inner tube
- jumper

23

Clever Elves

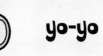 aeroplane

 bag of coal

 yo-yo

 bicycle

 cookies

kitten

fishing rod

 ornament

reindeer

mouse

 train

 Mrs. Claus' glasses

Ginger Joy

- bow tie
- poinsettia
- heart
- mug
- mailbox
- cherry
- wreath
- hat
- glasses
- stocking
- ribbon
- button

26

pizza

bell

coffee cup

pine tree

apple

candy cane

beefburger

ring

flag

lion

Statue of liberty

 dice

Ho-Ho Holiday

striped beach towel

sunscreen

conch shell

flag

crab

snorkel and mask

iguana

camera

sailing boat

shark fin

Frisbee

life jacket

FOUND EVERYTHING?

Not quite! Flip back and see if you can find these sneaky items.

car

lizard

cupcake

T. rex

hot-air balloon

flag

ginger bear

mermaid

pelican

skater

camp fire

robot

cow

baseball bat

starfish

cockerel